TALES OF GODS AND DEMONS FROM
INDIAN MYTHOLOGY

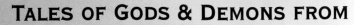

CONTENTS

Churning of the Ocean

CHURNING OF THE OCEAN

From times immemorial, the gods have stood for good and the demons have stood for evil. Once, when the gods and the demons were not immortal, an argument broke out between them as to who is superior to whom.

The argument continued for many days. Meanwhile, the great sage Durvasa went to meet the king of Gods, Indra, and gave him a garland. Indra gave the garland to his elephant to play with. Seeing this, Durvasa flew into a rage and cursed Indra.

Indra apologised to Durvasa but the curse couldn't be taken back. Getting horrified, the gods went to Lord Brahma and asked for help. Brahma directed them to Lord Vishnu. So, Indra and other gods went to Vishnu and told him about the curse.

After some thought, Vishnu said,
"If you drink 'Amrit', the nectar of
immortality, you will become immortal,
and then the demons won't defeat you!"
"Where do we get that?" asked Indra.
"You will have to churn the ocean!"
replied Vishnu.

When the demons heard about the nectar of immortality, they readily agreed to help the gods to churn the ocean. Now they requested the mount Mandara to become the churning rod. The mighty serpent Vasuki agreed to be used as a rope.

Mandara was placed at the middle of the ocean. Vasuki coiled around the huge mountain. The demons lined up, holding the serpent on the side of its head and the gods lined up holding its tail. When all were set, the churning began.

But soon, Mandara started sinking as there was no solid support beneath it. "Oh, no! The mountain is slipping out of the rope!" cried the gods and the demons. Vishnu then took the form of a tortoise and balanced the mountain on his back.

The churning went on for a thousand years. Many things emerged from the ocean. At last emerged the great healer Dhanvantari, carrying the nectar of immortality in a jar. The gods and the demons were delighted.

Suddenly, the greedy demons snatched the jar from Dhanvantari and began running away. The gods asked them to give the jar. But the wicked demons refused to share the nectar with the gods. The gods were disappointed and worried.

Now Vishnu, in the form of a beautiful maiden Mohini, enchanted the demons and took the jar from them. The demons were excited at the thought of getting the nectar from the hands of Mohini. But Mohini gave all the nectar to the gods.

When the nectar was over, the demons realised that they had been tricked. They attacked the gods. But by now the gods had become immortal. They charged at the demons. Getting defeated, the demons fled away from there.

Brahma and The Two Demons

BRAHMA AND THE TWO DEMONS

Millions of years ago, there lived two demon brothers, Sunda and Upasunda, who loved each other intensely. They were of massive size and strength. They were so cruel that they would often attack the gods and the sages and harass them.

One day, the two brothers decided to usurp the heaven from the gods.
So, they attacked their kingdom.
The gods were not ready for this attack, so they were terrified.
Sunda and Upasunda managed to chase them out of the heaven.

The gods felt humiliated and dejected. One of them said, "We must plan and attack these two brothers and chase them out of our city." "Alright!" said the other. "Let's go to our king!" So, they all went to Indra and told him all that had happened.

When Indra heard about Sunda and Upasunda, he was worried. "It's not that easy to kill them!" he said. "They have a boon that they will only be killed if one kills the other. And that seems impossible, seeing their love for each other.

Let's go to Lord Brahma. He will definitely help us!

So, the gods, led by Indra, went to
Brahma. "Please do something, O Lord!
Get us rid of these two wicked
brothers!" the gods pleaded. At first,
Brahma was silent as he knew it wasn't
easy to deal with Sunda and Upasunda.

Suddenly Brahma thought, "The only way out is to create a rift between the two brothers!" So, he made a plan. Assuring the gods that his plan would surely work, Brahma asked them to send the celestial architect Vishwakarma to him.

As soon as Vishwakarma received Brahma's message, he presented himself before him. "I need your help, O great architect!" said Brahma. "Order me, O Lord!" Vishwakarma said. "Please create a celestial nymph!" Brahma said.

In no time, Vishwakarma created a celestial nymph. She was as beautiful as Brahma had expected. Brahma adorned the nymph with thousands of gems that enhanced her beauty. Then he breathed life into her and named her Tilottama.

Brahma then sent Tilottama to Sunda and Upasunda. By now, the two demons had dominated the three worlds. As soon as they saw Tilottama, they were mesmerized by her beauty and charm. Both of them wished to marry her.

"Sunda!" said Upasunda, "I am going to marry this maiden." "No, no! You can't!" cried Sunda, "I have already decided to marry her." Now, both the brothers began to fight. Tilottama became a bone of contention between them.

Brahma's plan worked well. Blinded
with lust and anger, both the brothers
attacked each other and got killed.
Up from the heavens, the gods
watched this and felt relieved. Thus,
the kingdom of gods was restored
to its peace and glory.

Prince Dhruva

PRINCE DHRUVA

Long ago, there lived king Uttanpad. He had two wives - Suniti, who had a son named Dhruva, and Suruchi, who had a son named Uttam. Suruchi was very beautiful. So, the king loved her and Uttam more than Suniti and Dhruva.

One day, Uttam was sitting on the king's lap. Dhruva also wanted to sit on his father's lap. When he came near the king, Suruchi shouted at him, "Lay off! You are not worthy of sitting on the king's lap. Uttam holds a higher position than you!"

Dhruva was heartbroken. He thought, "I shall pray to Lord Vishnu and ask for a position higher than Uttam, so I can sit on my father's lap." So, he walked out of the palace, into the forest. His mother, Suniti, tried to stop him. But the boy was firm.

After some miles, Dhruva reached the forest. Suddenly, he was stopped by Sage Narada. "Go back home!" Narada advised. "No! I won't!" said Dhruva. Narada told him that there was danger in the forest. But nothing could move Dhruva.

Surprised at the boy's adamance, Narada asked, "What will you do here?" Dhruva then told him how he had been thrown out by Suruchi. Narada felt sorry for the boy and consoled him. He taught him how to meditate and appease Lord Vishnu.

Dhruva concentrated on the Lord and chanted the sacred verse that Narada had taught him. He meditated for many months. The gods and demons were startled at the penance of the child. The gods feared he would take their position.

Getting worried, the gods went to Lord Vishnu and asked his help. Vishnu then appeared before Dhruva and said, "I am pleased with your penance, Dhruva! Ask what you may!" Dhruva narrated to Vishnu all that had happened.

Vishnu smiled at the boy's innocence. He said, "You definitely deserve a high position. May you become a polestar and shine at the North Pole, the highest place in the sky." Vishnu then blessed the boy and told him to go back home.

When Dhruva reached home, he was in for a pleasant surprise. His father was standing at the gate, waiting for him to return. "O Dhruva! My son!" he cried and welcomed him with open arms. From that day, Dhruva enjoyed the love of his father.

Days and months passed... years rolled on. Meanwhile, Prince Uttam was killed while hunting. Suruchi was also killed in a forest fire when she went searching for her son, Uttam. Dhruva was crowned the king. He ruled wisely for many years.

After carrying out his responsibilities well, at a ripe old age, Dhruva passed away. As promised by Vishnu, he was placed among the celestial stars and planets in the sky. From that day, Dhruva shines at the North Pole and is called 'Dhruva Tara'.

Shiva and Kali

SHIVA AND KALI

Once, there lived two powerful demons, Shumbha and Nishumbha. They would often attack the heavens and torture the gods. Once, they attacked Indra, the king of gods, and seized his vast empire. Many gods were driven out of the heavens.

Indra and other inmates of the heavens were terrified. "Let's go to Lord Shiva's wife, the powerful goddess Parvati. She alone can let us out of this peril," said Indra. Others agreed with Indra and so they all rushed to Goddess Parvati.

Parvati patiently listened to their woes and worries. Then she said, "Don't worry! Shumbha and Nishumbha will soon meet their end!" The goddess recreated an image of herself and called her 'Ambika'. "She will help you!" Parvati assured Indra.

Ambika was very beautiful. When the demons heard of her beauty, they came running to see her. Two ferocious demons, Chanda and Munda, who worked for Shumbha and Nishumbha, also came to see Ambika.

Chanda and Munda informed their masters about Ambika. Shumbha and Nishumbha sent a messenger, Sugreev, to bring Ambika to their place.
"Hah, if you want to take me along, you will have to defeat me first," said Ambika to Sugreev.

Sugreev went to Chanda and Munda and told them what Ambika had told. "Uh! We will have to fight with a woman?" mocked Chanda. "A mere woman! Ha! Ha!" added Munda. "Let our masters decide!" said Sugreev. So, they informed their masters.

Shumbha and Nishumbha then sent another demon, 'Dhoomralochan', to fetch Ambika. As soon as Dhoomralochan approached Ambika, she gave him a scornful look. Her eyes emitted fire that burnt Dhoomralochan to ashes.

Getting worried, Shumbha and Nishumbha ordered Chanda and Munda to attack Ambika and capture her. Ambika now acquired a ferocious form, called 'Kali', and beheaded Chanda and Munda. She hacked off their entire army.

Seeing Kali's violent form, Shumbha and Nishumbha tried to run away. "You can't escape!" cried Kali, as she caught them and hacked off their heads. The gods felt relief. But now, there was another terrible sight. Kali was in a frenzy and ran amuck.

She went on killing the demons, whoever came in her way. The gods now feared that if this continued, Kali may even attack them. So, they all went to Lord Shiva and begged, "Please stop this dance of death, O Lord! Only you can control Kali!"

To stop Kali, Shiva lay down in her path. Blinded with anger, Kali didn't see him and stepped upon him. Only then did she regain her senses. "Oh no!" said Kali, as her tongue came out in regret. Thus, Shiva calmed down the angered goddess

The Trishanku Heaven

THE TRISHANKU HEAVEN

Long ago, there lived King Trishanku, the ruler of the lunar dynasty in ancient India. One day, Trishanku went to his Guru Vasishtha and said, "I want to leave this earth, not as a soul, but in my human form." Vasishtha was startled.

"But that's unholy. I can't do that!" said Vasishtha. "You have to do it, O great sage! For my sake!" Trishanku insisted. "That's just impossible!" said Vasishtha. But Trishanku was not ready to listen. He decided to approach Vasishtha's sons.

So, Trishanku went to Vasishtha's sons and put forth his request. They too felt irritated at the unreasonable demand. "How dare you come to us when our father has already turned down your demand?" they shouted at Trishanku.

Vasishtha's sons cursed Trishanku to become an untouchable. The next morning, Trishanku woke up a deformed man, his skin had darkened, his hair had fallen out, he had bruises all over his body and his jewels had turned into bones.

As soon as Trishanku came out of his royal chambers, the guards shouted at him, "Who are you? What are you doing in here?" "I am your king!" said Trishanku. But no one believed him. The guards chased him out of the palace.

Trishanku felt helpless and horrified. But he was still keen on leaving the earth in his human form. So, he went to Sage Vishwamitra and told him how Vasishtha had turned down his demand and how his sons had punished him.

Now, Vishwamitra was Vasishtha's arch-rival. So, he decided to fulfill Trishanku's demand. At first, he tried to convince the gods to accept Trishanku in heaven. But when they refused, the sage, using his powers, made Trishanku to rise to heaven.

But this was not to be. As soon as he reached the threshold of heaven, the gods pushed him down. They were not willing to let in a mortal body. Trishanku would have dashed to earth and died, had Vishwamitra not saved him.

Vishwamitra was angry at the gods.
So, he froze Trishanku midway between
the earth and heavens. "Hunh! Let the
gods keep their heavens. I shall make
my own heaven for Trishanku," he
thought. And he planned to make the
'Trishanku Heaven'.

The gods were terrified of Vishwamitra's powers. So, they ran to the holy sage, Brihaspati, and said, "Vishwamitra is going to create his own heaven. He can do anything! Please stop him!" Brihaspati then intervened into the matter.

Paying heed to Brihaspati's advice, Vishwamitra gave up his plan. Trishanku was thus deprived of his unreasonable wish. He became a constellation and was fated to remain fixed in the sky, hanging between the earth and the heavens.

Nala and Damayanti

NALA AND DAMAYANTI

Nala, the king of Nishada, was a bachelor. One day, a Brahmin came to Nala's court and informed him about a beautiful princess, named Damayanti. "Her father is soon going to hold her swayamvara, O king!" said the Brahmin.

The Brahmin praised Diamanti so much that Nala fell in love with the princess, even without seeing her. He began to wait eagerly for her swayamvara. One day, Nala was sitting alone in the royal garden, lost in thoughts. A swan noticed him.

"Why are you sad, O king?" asked the swan. Nala told him all about his love for Damayanti. "Can I help you in any way?" asked the swan. "Please inform her about my love for her?" said the king. So, the swan carried the king's message to her.

Soon, the swan returned with a favourable reply from the princess. "She too happens to love you, O king!" said the swan. "Her father will conduct the swayamvara soon, and she will choose you as her husband." Nala was delighted to hear this.

Meanwhile, Damayanti pretended to be sick. Many physicians examined her but found nothing wrong. Finally, Damayanti's parents understood that it was time for her to get married. So, her father instantly announced her swayamvara.

The invitation for swayamvara was extended to all the neighbouring kings and princes. King Nala was also invited. His joy knew no bounds. But to avoid embarrassment, he hid his excitement. "Get my horse ready!" Nala ordered.

On his way, Nala was stopped by the gods - Indra, Varuna, Agni and Yama. "We also shall be present in the swayamvara!" they said. "Go to Damayanti's chamber and ask her to choose any one of us!" Now Nala was in a fix. But he couldn't disobey them.

The gods instantly transported Nala to Damayanti's chamber. As soon as Nala and Damayanti met, they felt true love for each other. But Nala had to pass on the message to the princess. So, he hesitantly told her about the gods.

At the stipulated time, many kings and princes gathered for the swayamvara. King Nala and the four gods were also present. But the four gods had disguised themselves as Nala. So, when Damayanti came with a garland, she was puzzled.

Damayanti carefully looked at all the five Nalas. Finally, she garlanded the real one. "How could you spot out the actual Nala?" asked the gods. "It was simple," replied Damayanti. "Nala looked at me normally, while you all had godly unblinking eyes."

The gods appreciated Damayanti's intelligence, and said, "You truly deserve to marry Nala!" They blessed the couple and returned to heaven. Nala and Damayanti got married. They returned to the kingdom of Nishada and lived happily.

Hanuman Burns Lanka

HANUMAN BURNS LANKA

Once, Ravana, the demon king of Lanka had abducted Sita, the wife of Prince Rama of Ayodhya. While searching for Sita, Rama and his brother Lakshmana met the mighty Monkey God Hanuman. They reached the ocean, across which lay the city of Lanka.

Being a great devotee of Rama, Hanuman couldn't see his anguish. "Don't worry, Lord!" he said. "I will leap across the ocean to meet Mother Sita and assure her that you will soon rescue her. " Rama liked the idea. He gave his ring to Hanuman.

Hanuman used his powers and expanded his body to a huge size. Then he flew across the ocean, to Lanka. Many hurdles came in his way. One of them was Surasa, the mother of all serpents. Surasa blocked Hanuman's way and opened her mouth.

"I won't let you go unless you get into my mouth!" she hissed. "And once you get inside, you can't come out. Ha! Ha! Ha!" But clever Hanuman shrunk to the size of a fly, went inside Surasa's mouth and came out, even before she could realise.

Surasa had been testing Hanuman.
She blessed him and let him go.
Soon, Hanuman landed in Lanka.
"The guards can easily identify me,
if I retain my size," he thought.
So, he reduced himself to the size
of a fly and entered into the city.

Hanuman flew across the city, searching for Sita. Finally, he found her sitting under a tree in a garden called 'Ashoka Vatika'. Hanuman hid in the branches of a tree and watched, as Ravana threatened Sita to marry him. But Sita kept quiet.

As soon as Ravana left, Hanuman dropped Rama's ring in front of Sita. "Oh, this is my lord's ring! He has come to save me!" thought Sita, looking around. Then Hanuman came before Sita and gave her Rama's message. Sita was overwhelmed.

"Come with me, Mother!" Hanuman suggested, "I shall safely carry you out of Lanka." But Sita wanted Rama to come there, kill Ravana and free the other innocent captives too. She gave her necklace to Hanuman as a symbol.

Now, it so happened that Ravana's guards caught Hanuman and brought him to the court. "I am a messenger of Rama!" said Hanuman. "Make peace with him and free Sita." Hearing this, Ravana got angry and ordered Hanuman's tail to be set on fire.

Ravana's men carried out his orders. They wrapped Hanuman's tail with a long piece of cloth dipped in inflammable oil, and set fire to it. Inside his mind, Hanuman had decided to avenge this insult. He instantly began to expand his body.

Suddenly, he began to hop from rooftop to rooftop, waving his blazing tail, setting the entire city on fire, except for the garden where Sita was staying. Then Hanuman dipped his tail in the ocean and put off the fire. He then flew back to his Lord Rama.

Dushyant and Shakuntala

DUSHYANT AND SHAKUNTALA

Shakuntala was the daughter of Maneka, a celestial nymph. One day, Indra called back Maneka to the heavens. So, Maneka had no choice but to leave Shakuntala in the ashram of the holy sage, Rishi Kanva, who would be her foster father.

Shakuntala grew up into a beautiful maiden. One day, she saw a deer wounded by an arrow. The soft-hearted maiden ran to rescue the deer. Just then there came a king named Dushyant, who had wounded the deer.

Realising his mistake, Dushyant agreed to stay in the ashram and nurse the deer. As the days passed, he fell in love with Shakuntala and married her. They were happy. But soon it was time for the king to leave. He couldn't take Shakuntala along.

A few days later, Shakuntala realised she was pregnant. Her joy knew no bounds. She began to dream about her life with her husband and child. The whole day, she would be sitting alone, occupied in the thoughts of her loving husband.

One day, Sage Durvasa visited the ashram. But Shakuntala, lost in her sweet dreams, didn't notice him. Getting angry, Durvasa cursed her, "Let the person in your dreams forget you!" Realising her blunder, Shakuntala asked for forgiveness.

Shakuntala decided to meet Dushyant. But there was another misfortune awaiting her. While crossing the river, her ring slipped off her finger and fell into the water. Unaware of it, Shakuntala was lost in the sweet thoughts of meeting the king.

The curse won't hold good! My husband will recognise me as soon as he sees the ring that he gave me.

Shakuntala reached Dushyant's palace.
"Who are you?" asked Dushyant,
having forgotten her. Shakuntala lifted
her hand to show him the ring...
But lo! There was nothing she could
show him to remind him who she was.
She had to return sadly.

Some months later, Shakuntala gave birth to a son. She named him 'Bharat'. Meanwhile, a fisherman one day found a ring as he chopped a fish. "Oh, this ring bears our king's name!" he exclaimed. So, he carried the ring to King Dushyant.

As soon as Dushyant took the ring in his hand, the memories of yesteryears resumed to him and he uttered, "O my Shakuntala!" The king then prepared to leave for the ashram. He took some of his chosen men along with him.

When Dushyant reached the ashram, he saw a small boy playing with tigers, counting their teeth. Dushyant was amazed at the boy's courage. "Who are you, O brave boy?" he asked. "I am King Dushyant's son!" replied the boy.

Just then, Shakuntala came out of her hut. "O Shakuntala!" cried the king. "At last you recognised me, my lord!" she sobbed. They hugged each other. Dushyant was glad to have such a brave son. He then took his family to his palace.

King Harishchandra

KING HARISHCHANDRA

Long ago, there lived King Harishchandra. He was pious, charitable, honest and devout. He was famous for his undeterred truthfulness. Harishchandra ruled wisely and his kingdom was a happy one. His people praised him and had faith in him.

Harishchandra's fame grew far and wide. When it reached the ears of Indra, the king of gods, he became jealous. Indra went to Sage Vishwamitra and said, "Let's see if Harishchandra stands by truth and commitment even in misfortunes!"

Vishwamitra agreed to Indra. With the help of his special powers, Vishwamitra appeared in Harishchandra's dreams that night and said, "I want your entire kingdom, O charitable king!" "Take it, O holy sage!" Harishchandra said.

The next morning, Vishwamitra arrived at Harishchandra's court and demanded his kingdom. Bound by his commitment, Harishchandra left the kingdom with his wife and son. But that was not all. Now the sage asked for a charity.

Having given away his entire kingdom, all that Harishchandra had was his family. So, he sold his wife and son to a Brahmin and gave the earning to Vishwamitra, in charity. But Vishwamitra was still not satisfied. "Give me more!" he said.

Harishchandra was in a fix. How would he give more charity to the sage! Perhaps, the only way to arrange money was to sell himself. So, Harishchandra sold himself to a person who cremated the dead bodies and gave the money to Vishwamitra.

Now, Harishchandra had to work under his master and cremate the dead bodies. One day, his wife, who had been working as a maid at the Brahmin's place, found her son dead. Wailing, she carried her son's body to the cremation grounds.

When Harishchandra saw his son dead, he was deeply aggrieved. His hands trembled at the thought of cremating his own child. But he would never forego his duty. So, composing himself, he said, "You have to pay me for the task."

Harishchandra knew his wife was helpless. But he would not betray his master. So, he insisted that the payment be made. His wife then tore a piece of cloth off her veil and offered as the payment. Harishchandra accepted it.

With tearful eyes, Harishchandra prepared the pyre. Just then, there appeared Lord Vishnu, Indra and Vishwamitra. "Your devotion towards duty is unmatched, Harishchandra!" said Vishnu. He then brought his son back to life.

Harishchandra and his wife were overjoyed. Indra and Vishwamitra returned his kingdom too. Thus, by following truth and righteousness, Harishchandra regained all that he had lost and lived happily with his family.

Presented by:

....

On the occasion of:

....